Maths Age 6-7

Melissa Blackwood, Liz Dawson & Stephen Monaghan

In a strange place, not too far from here, lives a scare of monsters.

A 'scare' is what some people call a group of monsters, but these monsters are really very friendly once you get to know them.

They are a curious bunch – they look very unusual, but they are quite like you and me, and they love learning new things and having fun.

In this book you will go on a learning journey with the monsters and you are sure to have lots of fun along the way.

Do not forget to visit our website to find out more about all the monsters and to send us photos of you in your monster mask or the monsters that you draw and make!

Contents

Numbers and Number Words

Litmus is learning to spell number words using magnetic letters.

80 eighty

He has nearly finished, when Zak runs into the board and they all fall onto the floor in a pile!

1 **a** Draw lines to match the numbers to the number words.

| nine | four | seven | one | six |

(9) (1) (6) (7) (2) (4) (10) (5) (8) (3)

| eight | ten | two | five | three |

b Draw lines to match these tens numbers and number words.

| forty | twenty | eighty | sixty | thirty |

(50) (90) (60) (70) (100) (10) (20) (40) (30) (80)

| ten | seventy | one hundred | ninety | fifty |

2 Help Litmus write the number words for the numbers.
The first one has been done for you.

a 67   sixty-seven

b 34

c 28

d 73

e 59

3 Read the number words and write the numbers in the boxes.

a forty-two

b sixty-one

c ninety-seven

d fifty-three

Fun Zone!

It is time for some target fun!

Great work!
You can now
find and colour
Shape 1 on the
Monster Match
page!

Target Fun

You will need a pen, a large piece of paper and soft toys filled with plastic beans.
Ask an adult to help when needed.

1 Draw 3 circles inside each other on a large piece of paper.
2 Write a score inside each circle. The number should be small in the outside circle and get bigger as you go in.
3 Throw the soft toys at the circles.
4 Add up your score after 3 throws. The highest score wins!

More or Less

Litmus chooses 5 cards from a pack of number cards and lays them out.

| 2 | 5 | 7 | 3 | 10 |

He says '2 is less than 5, 5 is less than 7, 7 is more than 3 and 3 is less than 10.'

Kora says you can use symbols instead of words:

2 is **less than** 5   7 is **more than** 3

2 **<** 5   7 **>** 3

1 Put the **more than** or **less than** symbol between each pair of numbers.

a 16 ☐ 27   c 87 ☐ 88   e 78 ☐ 97

b 34 ☐ 12   d 65 ☐ 42   f 51 ☐ 50

2 Nano has jumbled up all the number cards!
Write the numbers in order, putting the smallest number first.
The first one has been done for you.

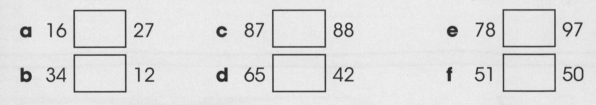

a 41 20 12 87 42 | 12 | ☐ | ☐ | ☐ | ☐ |

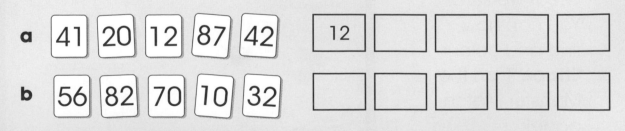

b 56 82 70 10 32 | ☐ | ☐ | ☐ | ☐ | ☐ |

Hundreds, Tens and Units

Kora wants to know how many buttons are in a bag that she has found.

She puts the buttons in piles of 10.

When she has 10 piles of buttons, she puts them in a box.

There are 100 buttons in a box, so Kora can write 3 numbers: a **hundreds** number, a **tens** number and a **units** number.

I box of buttons	4 piles of buttons	5 buttons	
1 hundred	4 tens	5 units	= 145

1 Count how many buttons there are.

a

b

2 Write the number of buttons there are.

a

b

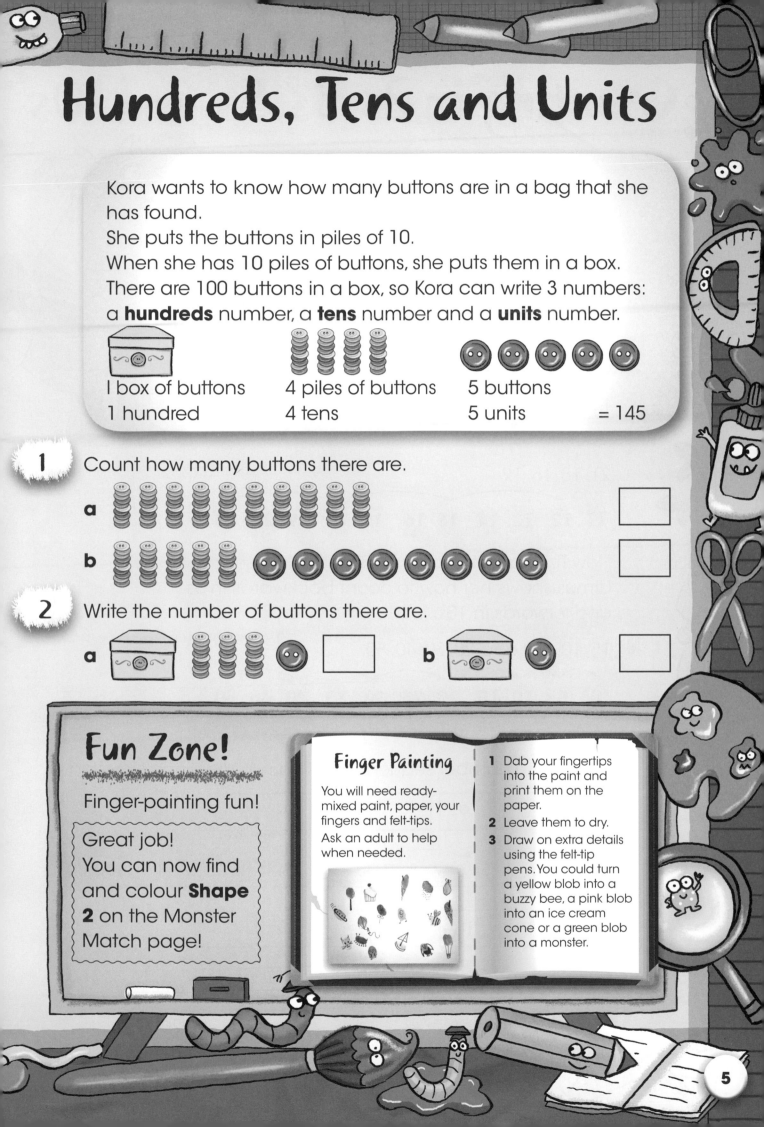

Fun Zone!

Finger-painting fun!

Great job!
You can now find and colour **Shape 2** on the Monster Match page!

Finger Painting

You will need ready-mixed paint, paper, your fingers and felt-tips.
Ask an adult to help when needed.

1 Dab your fingertips into the paint and print them on the paper.
2 Leave them to dry.
3 Draw on extra details using the felt-tip pens. You could turn a yellow blob into a buzzy bee, a pink blob into an ice cream cone or a green blob into a monster.

Counting in 2s, 3s, 5s and 10s

Litmus is helping Tizz count in 2s and 3s.
Tizz tries to count on her fingers
but soon runs out!
Litmus shows Tizz an example of how to
count forwards in 2s using a **number line**.

1, 3, 5, 7, 9

0 1 2 3 4 5 6 7 8 9 10

Tizz can also use a number line to count
backwards in 3s.

21, 18, 15, 12

11 12 13 14 15 16 17 18 19 20 21

Now Tizz wants to count in 5s and 10s.
Litmus shows her how to count backwards in 5s
and forwards in 10s.

15, 10, 5, 0 and 20, 30, 40, 50

0 5 10 15 20 25 30 35 40 45 50

1 Complete the number sequence on the number lines provided.

a

| 3 | 6 | 9 | | | | |

0 1 2 3 4 5 6 7 8 9 10 11 12 13 14 15 16 17 18 19 20 21

b

| 20 | 18 | 16 | | | | |

0 1 2 3 4 5 6 7 8 9 10 11 12 13 14 15 16 17 18 19 20 21

2 Use the number line to write the next 4 numbers in the sequence.

0 1 2 3 4 5 6 7 8 9 10 11 12 13 14 15 16 17 18 19 20 21

a | 2 | 4 | 6 | 8 | | | |
b | 3 | 6 | 9 | | | | |
c | 12 | 10 | 8 | | | | |

3 Complete these number sequences.

a | 10 | 15 | 20 | | | |
b | 2 | 12 | | | | |
c | 59 | 49 | 39 | | | |

4 Write the next 4 numbers in the sequence.

a | 3 | 8 | 13 | | | | |
b | 68 | 58 | 48 | | | | |
c | 2 | 7 | 12 | | | | |
d | 1 | 11 | 21 | | | | |

Fun Zone!

Create your own monster jingle using wooden spoons, pots and pans.

Good work!
You can now find and colour **Shape 3** on the Monster Match page!

Addition

Mum is picking mumble fruit from the fruit tree outside.

There are 2 baskets of fruit on the ground by the tree.
One basket has 23 mumble fruits, the other one has 16.
Litmus counts the fruit she is picking.

Counting how many there are **altogether** is called **addition**.
Litmus can add larger numbers together using **column addition**.

He puts the numbers under each other.

tens ⟶ | T | U | ⟵ **units**
|---|---|
| 2 | 3 |
| + 1 | 6 |

Add up the **tens** ⟶ | 3 | 9 | ⟵ Add up the **units** first

Altogether there are 39 mumble fruits from the mumble fruit tree.

1 Add these numbers together using the column addition method.

a

	T	U
	3	6
+	5	3

b

	T	U
	7	2
+	1	4

c

	T	U
	6	4
+	2	1

2 Litmus knows the pairs of numbers that make 10.
Write the other number that adds up to make 10.

a 4 + ☐ = 10   **c** 7 + ☐ = 10

b 2 + ☐ = 10   **d** 1 + ☐ = 10

3 Litmus knows the other number that makes 100.
Write the other number that adds up to make 100.

a 30 + ☐ = 100   **c** 20 + ☐ = 100

b 50 + ☐ = 100   **d** 40 + ☐ = 100

4 Fizz and Tizz have been helping Mum pick the mumble fruit.
Fizz has picked 13 fruits and Tizz has picked 21.

How many have they picked altogether? Use the column addition method to find the answer.

	T	U
+		

Fun Zone!

Now it is time to play the Torch Tig game!

Fantastic!
You can now find and colour **Shape 4** on the Monster Match page!

Torch Tig

You will need a dark space (or wait until it is night time), a torch and a base (such as a flag or beanbag).
Ask an adult to help when needed.

1 Put the base in the middle of the playing space.
2 One person takes the torch and stands guard by the base.
3 Other players spread out and try to get close to the base without their movement being seen.
4 If the person with the torch shines it on a moving player, they are out!

Subtraction

Litmus is working out some monster subtraction sums in the lab.
He knows that when he subtracts he must **take away** or **count backwards**.

Dad says 48 – 12 = 36 and shows Litmus how to work this out on a number line.

He starts at 48 and counts 12 steps backwards on the number line.
He lands on 36.

30 31 32 33 34 35 36 37 38 39 40 41 42 43 44 45 46 47 48 49 50

So, 48 – 12 = 36.

1 Answer the following questions using the number line below.

30 31 32 33 34 35 36 37 38 39 40 41 42 43 44 45 46 47 48 49 50

a 45 – 8 =

b 36 – 4 =

c 48 – 13 =

d 48 – 9 =

e 47 – 7 =

f 39 – 8 =

g 42 – 11 =

h 46 – 13 =

2 Now use your subtraction skills to answer the following word problems.
Use the number line in **1** to help you.

a  Nano has 46 stickers and then loses 7.
How many stickers does Nano have now? ☐

b Kora has 45 books and gives 14 to Poggo.
How many books does Kora have left? ☐

c Mum goes to the shop and buys 35 DVDs.
Then she returns 5 DVDs.
How many DVDs does Mum have now? ☐

d Gran has 47 buttons on her shelf.
Poggo uses 13.
How many buttons does Gran have left? ☐

Fun Zone!

Have fun making a button animal!

Excellent work! You can now find and colour **Shape 5** on the Monster Match page!

Button Animal

You will need lots of buttons, a piece of paper, pens and glue.

Ask an adult to help when needed.

1 Glue the buttons on a piece of paper to make the animal face.

2 Add extra detail with pens.

Multiplication

Litmus is showing Fizz how to count mini-monsters in the wild wood using **arrays**. Arrays are when pictures are used to show groups in **rows** and **columns**, like this.

$4 \times 2 = 8$

Litmus shows Fizz that he can use arrays to work out his 2, 5 and 10 times tables.

$2 \times 5 = 10$ $2 \times 10 = 20$

1 Use the arrays to help Fizz find the totals.

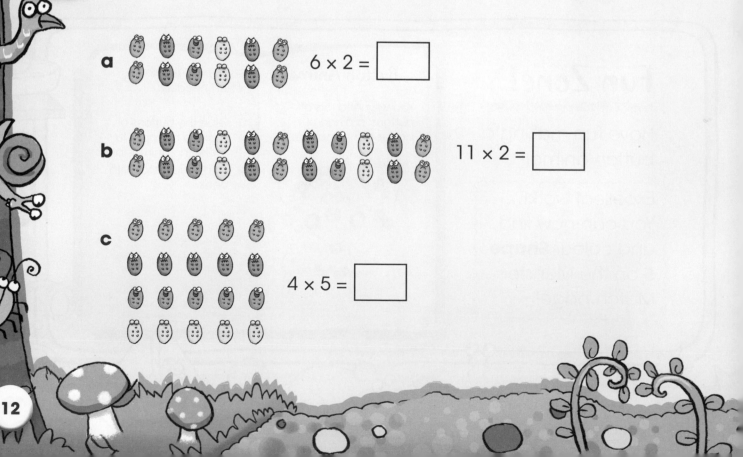

a $6 \times 2 = \boxed{}$

b $11 \times 2 = \boxed{}$

c $4 \times 5 = \boxed{}$

Division

Fizz is sharing her Monster Sports Cards with the other monsters.

When we **share** things out equally, we call it **dividing**.

Fizz shares 50 sports cards equally between 5.

Fizz	Poggo	Tizz	Litmus	Kora

Each of them gets 10 sports cards, so Fizz knows that 50 ÷ 5 = 10.

1 Help Fizz share the Monster Sports Cards out equally.

Litmus   Tizz

20 ÷ 2 = [   ]

Fun Zone!

Have fun with straw painting!

Monsterific! You can now find and colour **Shape 6** on the Monster Match page!

Straw Painting

You will need ready-mixed paint, water, paper, a paintbrush and a straw. Ask an adult to help when needed.

1 Mix a little water with the paint to make it a bit runnier.
2 Use the paintbrush to dab the runny paint onto the paper.
3 Use the straw to blow the paint around the paper.
4 You could use brown paint to make a tree, and stick leaves on afterwards or make a monster with lots of legs.

Monster Challenge 1

1 Match the word to the correct number.

18	sixty-seven
90	fifty-five
49	forty-nine
67	eighteen
55	ninety

2 Write down how many hundreds, tens and units each number has. The first one has been done for you.

Number	Hundreds	Tens	Units
243	2	4	3
356			
812			
999			
107			

3 Use the symbols for **more than >** and **less than <** to show which number is bigger.

a 18 ☐ 9   **c** 35 ☐ 99

b 89 ☐ 16   **d** 53 ☐ 78

4 Complete the gaps in the sequence.

a	6	9	12			21
b	90	80			50	40
c		25		35	40	45

5 Use the column addition method to add the following numbers.

a

	T	U
	4	5
+	2	2

b

	T	U
	1	7
+	5	1

c

	T	U
	3	4
+	4	3

6 Using your knowledge of the 'x' symbol, complete the following number sentences.

a $8 \times 2 =$

d $12 \times 2 =$

b $10 \times 5 =$

e $4 \times 5 =$

c $8 \times 10 =$

f $10 \times 10 =$

7 **a** Share the monster coins equally between Tizz, Fizz and Litmus.

Tizz   Fizz   Litmus

b Write down how many coins each monster gets.

Fun Fractions

Litmus is helping Fizz learn all about **fractions** using mini-monsters.

Litmus tells Fizz that she can find a fraction of an amount by sharing the number into groups.

He tells her that one **half** of 8 is 4 and he shares the mini-monsters out equally.

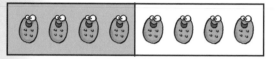

He can also write 'half' in numbers like this: $\frac{1}{2}$.

Then Litmus tells Fizz that one **quarter** of 8 is 2 and he shares the mini-monsters out equally.

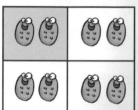

Litmus can also write 'one quarter' in numbers like this: $\frac{1}{4}$.

Litmus then tells Fizz that if he knows $\frac{1}{4}$ he can work out $\frac{3}{4}$ really easily!

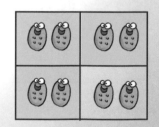

Litmus has 2 mini-monsters in each section, so $\frac{3}{4}$ of 8 is 6!

1 Find $\frac{1}{2}$, $\frac{1}{4}$ and $\frac{3}{4}$ of the number given using Litmus's helpful grids. The first one has been done for you.

a 12

$\frac{1}{2}$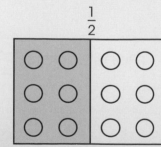

$\frac{1}{4}$

$\frac{3}{4}$

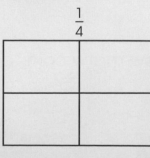

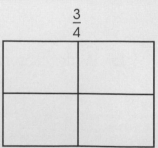

b 16 $\frac{1}{2}$ $\frac{1}{4}$ $\frac{3}{4}$

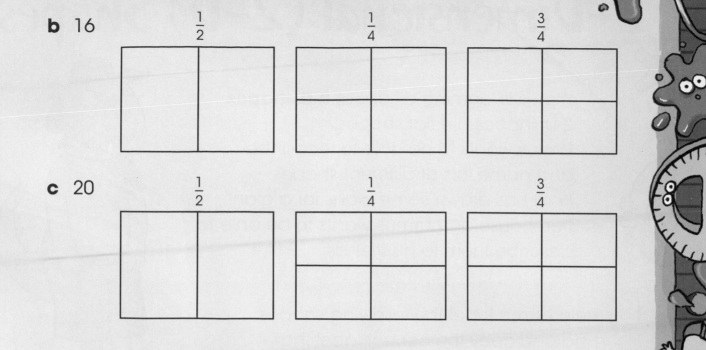

c 20 $\frac{1}{2}$ $\frac{1}{4}$ $\frac{3}{4}$

2 Litmus has been very busy and has made 20 paper aeroplanes.
Fizz, Tizz, Poggo and Litmus play with the paper aeroplanes.
Each monster will get one quarter of the aeroplanes.
How many aeroplanes is one quarter?

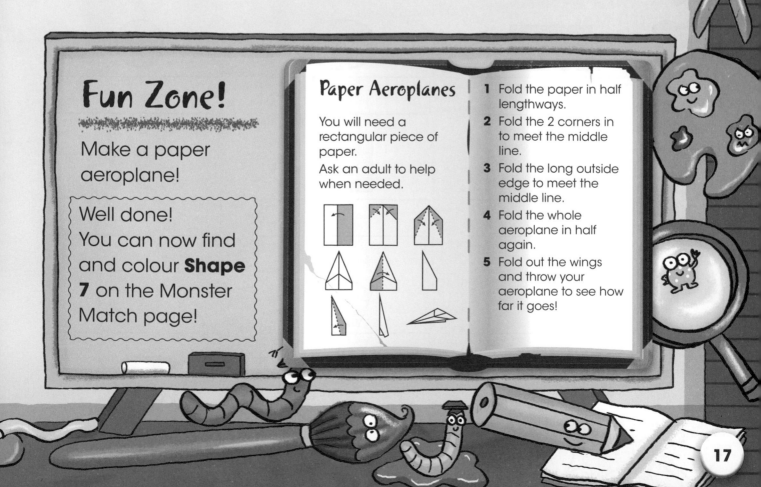

Fun Zone!

Make a paper aeroplane!

Well done! You can now find and colour **Shape 7** on the Monster Match page!

Paper Aeroplanes

You will need a rectangular piece of paper.

Ask an adult to help when needed.

1 Fold the paper in half lengthways.
2 Fold the 2 corners in to meet the middle line.
3 Fold the long outside edge to meet the middle line.
4 Fold the whole aeroplane in half again.
5 Fold out the wings and throw your aeroplane to see how far it goes!

2-Dimensional (2-D) Shapes

Litmus is learning all about **2-D shapes**.
2-D shapes are flat shapes.
Litmus wants to be able to recognise
and name lots of different shapes.
Kora has drawn some plans for a giant
tree house and Litmus wants to be able to
describe them to his friends.

1 Help Litmus label the following shapes.
Find and copy the correct label that
matches the 2-D shape.

square	oval	diamond
rectangle	star	circle
pentagon	hexagon	triangle

2 Dad has asked Litmus to tell him how many sides each shape has. Complete the following statements.

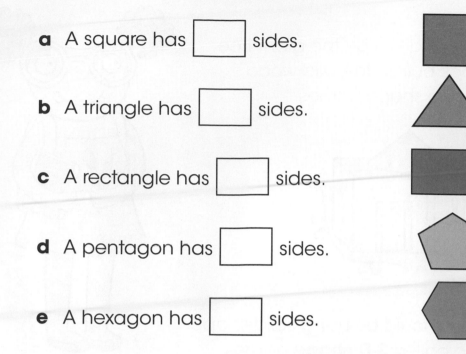

a A square has ☐ sides.

b A triangle has ☐ sides.

c A rectangle has ☐ sides.

d A pentagon has ☐ sides.

e A hexagon has ☐ sides.

Fun Zone!

Draw a monster using 2-D shapes in this space.

Stupendous shapes!
You can now find and colour **Shape 8** on the Monster Match page!

3-Dimensional (3-D) Shapes

Litmus wants to describe the giant tree house he has built in the wild wood with Kora using shape names.

Kora says he should be using solid shape names, also called **3-D shape** names. Kora shows Litmus how the **2-D shape** words and **3-D shape** words are linked.

A flat or curved side on a shape is called a **face**. A **cube** has 6 **square** faces.

This is an **edge**.

This is a **corner**.

1 Put a tick next to the 7 shape words that are 3-D shape names.

triangle ☐   cube ☐   square ☐   hexagon ☐

sphere ☐   rectangle ☐   cone ☐   pyramid ☐

cylinder ☐   cuboid ☐   pentagon ☐   triangular prism ☐

2 Let's see if Litmus was using the correct words to talk about his giant tree house.
Draw a smiley face if he is right, and a sad face if he is not.

a I used a cone at the top of my tree house.

b I used two squares at the bottom to make it extra strong.

3 Draw a line from the description to the correct shape.

a This shape has 6 faces and 8 corners.
The faces are rectangles.

b This shape has 2 faces.
One is curved and the other is flat.
There is 1 point and 1 edge.

c This shape has a triangle at each end.
It has 5 faces and 6 corners.

Fun Zone!

Now have fun feeling like a monster!

Excellent!
You can now find and colour **Shape 9** on the Monster Match page!

Monster Moods

You will need a box in the shape of a cube, coloured paper, glue, felt-tips and scissors.
Ask an adult to help when needed.

1 Cut out 6 squares of coloured paper, to fit the faces of the box.

2 Draw a different sort of face on each one. For example, a happy face, an excited face or a scary face.

3 Glue each face to a different side of the box.

4 Throw your mood cube and see which side lands face up. You have 30 seconds to act like a monster in that mood! For example, you could be a very excited Kora or a grumpy Webber!

Measuring Using a Scale

Tizz and Fizz are using a thermometer to measure the temperature of different Sneaky Sliding Sloops.
The bigger the number, the warmer it is.

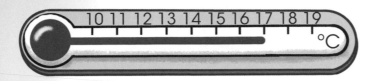

They are using a ruler to measure the length of the Sneaky Sliding Sloops in **centimetres**, which is written as **cm**.
Some of the Sneaky Sliding Sloops are too long for their centimetre ruler, so they use a metre ruler instead.
100 centimetres make 1 **metre**, which is written as **m**.

1 Write down the length of the Sneaky Sliding Sloops.
Remember to write **cm** after the number.

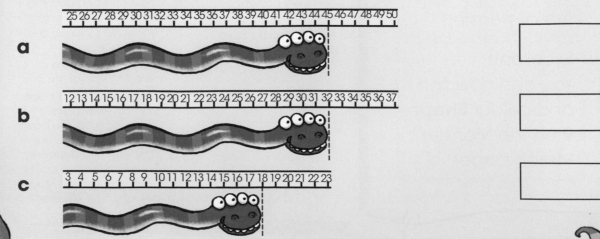

a

b

c

2 Measure the trees to find out which is the tallest one.
Write down the height of the trees.
Draw a Sneaky Sliding Sloop in the tallest tree.

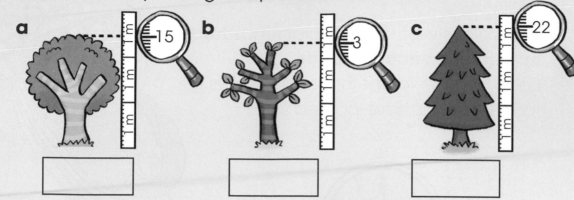

a [   ]   b [   ]   c [   ]

3 Fizz says she thinks the Sneaky Sliding Sloop is too hot.
Sneaky Sliding Sloops like to live at 17 °C.
Circle the place the Sneaky Sliding Sloop should live.

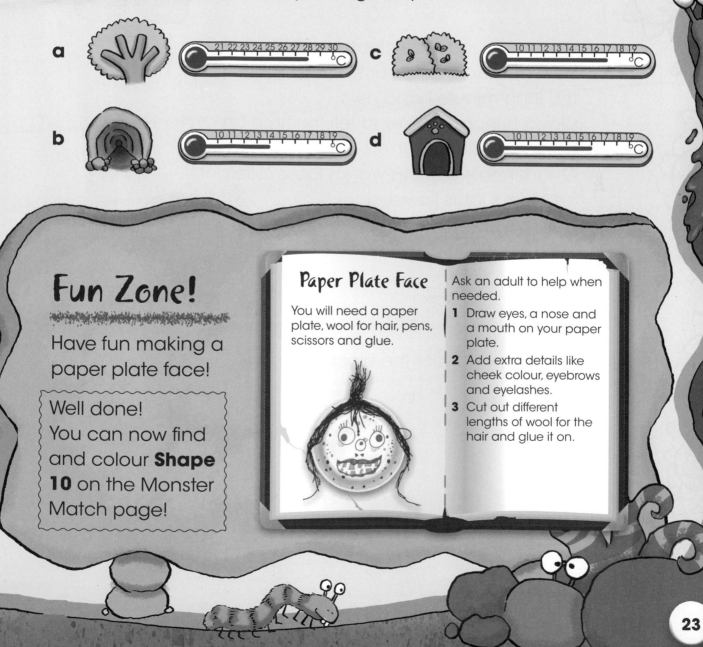

Fun Zone!

Have fun making a paper plate face!

Well done!
You can now find and colour **Shape 10** on the Monster Match page!

Paper Plate Face

You will need a paper plate, wool for hair, pens, scissors and glue.

Ask an adult to help when needed.

1 Draw eyes, a nose and a mouth on your paper plate.

2 Add extra details like cheek colour, eyebrows and eyelashes.

3 Cut out different lengths of wool for the hair and glue it on.

Telling the Time

Mum's lovely lotus flower clock has **hour**, **minute** and **second hands**.
Each number for the hour also shows that 5 minutes have passed.

Litmus can read the clock to tell the time.
He reads the short hour hand first, then the long minute hand next.
Litmus is learning how to tell the time on his new digital watch.
Quarter past 3 on his watch looks different on Mum's lotus flower clock.

digital watch   analogue clock

1 Write the times under the clocks in words.

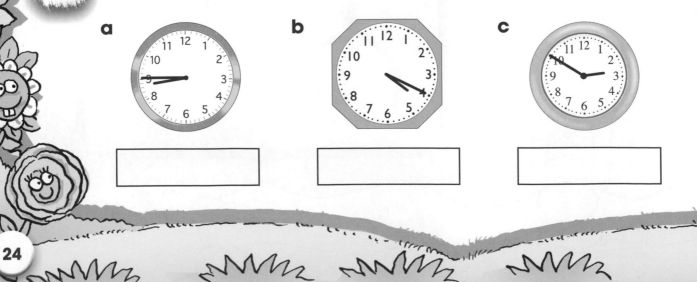

a

b

c

24

2 Now write the hands on the clocks.
Litmus's top tip is to start with the hour hand.

a

b

c

| half past 7 | quarter to 10 | 25 past 4 |

3 Draw lines from the digital times to the matching clock.

| 4 : 20 | 8 : 35 | 10 : 05 | 12 : 30 |

Fun Zone!

Use a clock with a second hand to time yourself for 1 minute.

Monsterific! You can now find and colour **Shape 11** on the Monster Match page!

Timer Fun

You will need a clock or watch with a second hand.
Ask an adult to help when needed.

Count how many things you can do in a minute.
Here are some ideas.

- Count how many star jumps you can do in 1 minute.
- Count how many snails you can find in 1 minute.
- Count how many numbers you can write in 1 minute.
- Count how many times you can write your name in 1 minute.

Monster Data

Fizz is trying to count how many of each type of ball she has at home.

First, she wants to produce a **tally chart**.
A tally chart allows Fizz to see how many of each type of ball she has.

Type	Tally	Number
●●●●	||||	4
●●●●●	卌	5

Fizz knows that when she gets to 5 she must place a line that strikes through the other lines.

After this, she wants to produce a **bar chart**.
A bar chart gives a visual image of how many of each type of ball Fizz has.

1 Fizz has forgotten to fill in the entire table!
Count how many of each type of ball she has and then complete the table.

Type	Tally	Number
●●●●	||||	
●●		
●●●●●●		6
●●●		3
●●●●●●●	卌 ||	

26

2 Now Fizz wants to put the information from the tally chart into a bar chart. Help Fizz by completing the bar chart. The first one has been done for you.

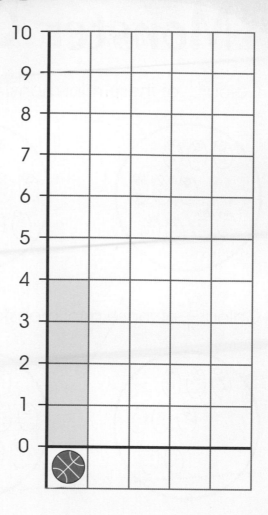

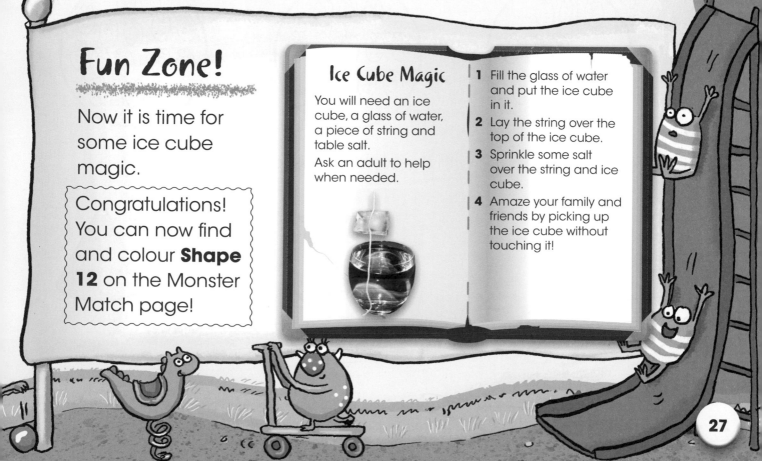

Fun Zone!

Now it is time for some ice cube magic.

Congratulations! You can now find and colour **Shape 12** on the Monster Match page!

Ice Cube Magic

You will need an ice cube, a glass of water, a piece of string and table salt.

Ask an adult to help when needed.

1 Fill the glass of water and put the ice cube in it.
2 Lay the string over the top of the ice cube.
3 Sprinkle some salt over the string and ice cube.
4 Amaze your family and friends by picking up the ice cube without touching it!

Monster Challenge 2

1 Colour $\frac{1}{2}$ of these mini-monsters in.

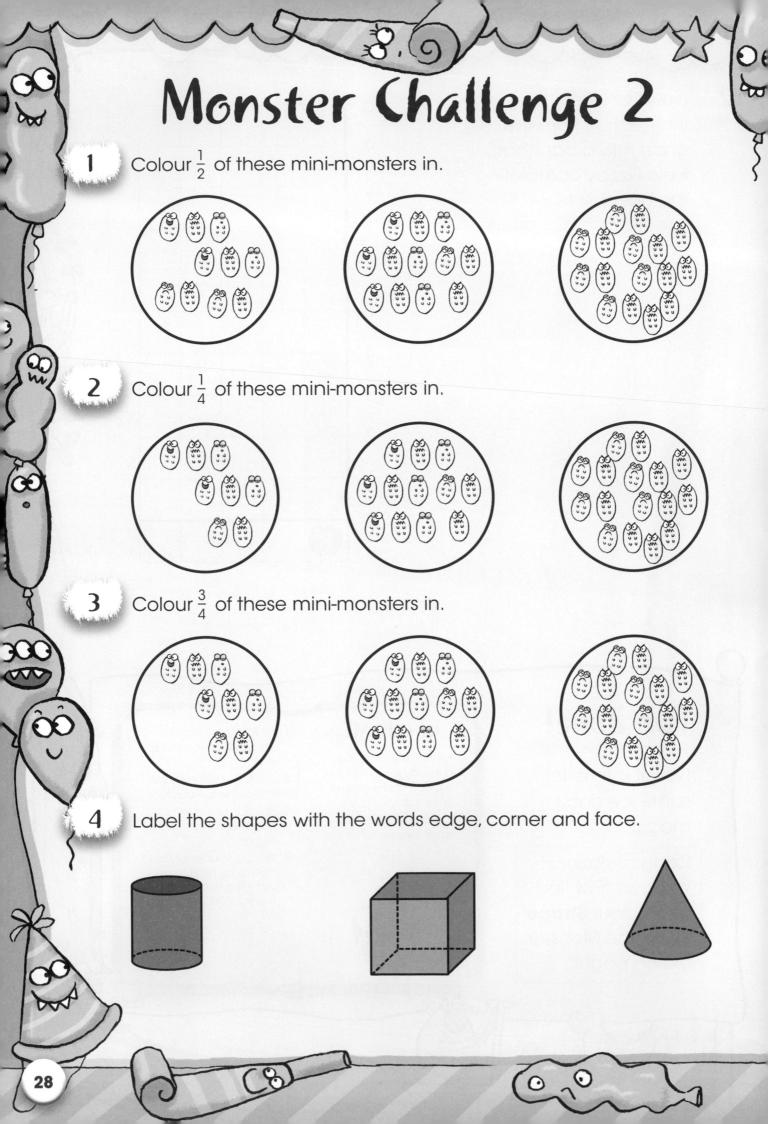

2 Colour $\frac{1}{4}$ of these mini-monsters in.

3 Colour $\frac{3}{4}$ of these mini-monsters in.

4 Label the shapes with the words edge, corner and face.

5 Read the scale and write the temperature in °C.
Tick the warmest temperature.

a 4 5 6 7 8 9 10 11 12 13 °C ☐

b 11 12 13 14 15 16 17 18 19 20 °C ☐

c 10 11 12 13 14 15 16 17 18 19 °C ☐

d 9 10 11 12 13 14 15 16 17 18 °C ☐

6 Read the times on the clocks and write the answers underneath.

a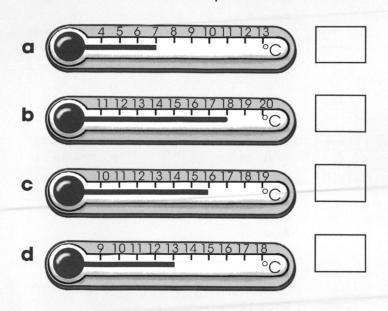

☐

b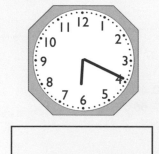

☐

7 Draw the hour and minute hands on the clocks to show the times.

a

| quarter past 9 |

b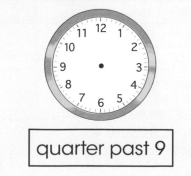

| half past 2 |

I knew you could do it!
You have made it to the end of the book.
You are a magnificent monster!

Answers

Page 2

1 a
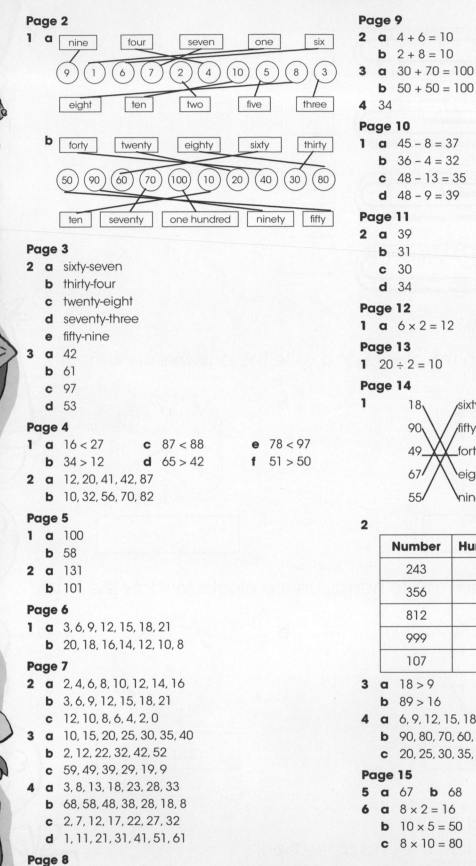

nine | four | seven | one | six

9 | 1 | 6 | 7 | 2 | 4 | 10 | 5 | 8 | 3

eight | ten | two | five | three

b

forty | twenty | eighty | sixty | thirty

50 | 90 | 60 | 70 | 100 | 10 | 20 | 40 | 30 | 80

ten | seventy | one hundred | ninety | fifty

Page 3

2 a sixty-seven
b thirty-four
c twenty-eight
d seventy-three
e fifty-nine

3 a 42
b 61
c 97
d 53

Page 4

1 a 16 < 27　**c** 87 < 88　**e** 78 < 97
b 34 > 12　**d** 65 > 42　**f** 51 > 50

2 a 12, 20, 41, 42, 87
b 10, 32, 56, 70, 82

Page 5

1 a 100
b 58
2 a 131
b 101

Page 6

1 a 3, 6, 9, 12, 15, 18, 21
b 20, 18, 16, 14, 12, 10, 8

Page 7

2 a 2, 4, 6, 8, 10, 12, 14, 16
b 3, 6, 9, 12, 15, 18, 21
c 12, 10, 8, 6, 4, 2, 0

3 a 10, 15, 20, 25, 30, 35, 40
b 2, 12, 22, 32, 42, 52
c 59, 49, 39, 29, 19, 9

4 a 3, 8, 13, 18, 23, 28, 33
b 68, 58, 48, 38, 28, 18, 8
c 2, 7, 12, 17, 22, 27, 32
d 1, 11, 21, 31, 41, 51, 61

Page 8

1 a 89　**b** 86　**c** 85

Page 9

2 a 4 + 6 = 10　　**c** 7 + 3 = 10
b 2 + 8 = 10　　**d** 1 + 9 = 10

3 a 30 + 70 = 100　**c** 20 + 80 = 100
b 50 + 50 = 100　**d** 40 + 60 = 100

4 34

Page 10

1 a 45 − 8 = 37　　**e** 47 − 7 = 40
b 36 − 4 = 32　　**f** 39 − 8 = 31
c 48 − 13 = 35　　**g** 42 − 11 = 31
d 48 − 9 = 39　　**h** 46 − 13 = 33

Page 11

2 a 39
b 31
c 30
d 34

Page 12

1 a 6 × 2 = 12　**b** 11 × 2 = 22　**c** 4 × 5 = 20

Page 13

1 20 ÷ 2 = 10

Page 14

1

18 — eighteen
90 — ninety
49 — forty-nine
67 — sixty-seven
55 — fifty-five

2

Number	Hundreds	Tens	Units
243	2	4	3
356	3	5	6
812	8	1	2
999	9	9	9
107	1	0	7

3 a 18 > 9　　**c** 35 < 99
b 89 > 16　　**d** 53 < 78

4 a 6, 9, 12, 15, 18, 21
b 90, 80, 70, 60, 50, 40
c 20, 25, 30, 35, 40, 45

Page 15

5 a 67　**b** 68　**c** 77
6 a 8 × 2 = 16　　**d** 12 × 2 = 24
b 10 × 5 = 50　　**e** 4 × 5 = 20
c 8 × 10 = 80　　**f** 10 × 10 = 100

7 a Fizz   Tizz   Litmus

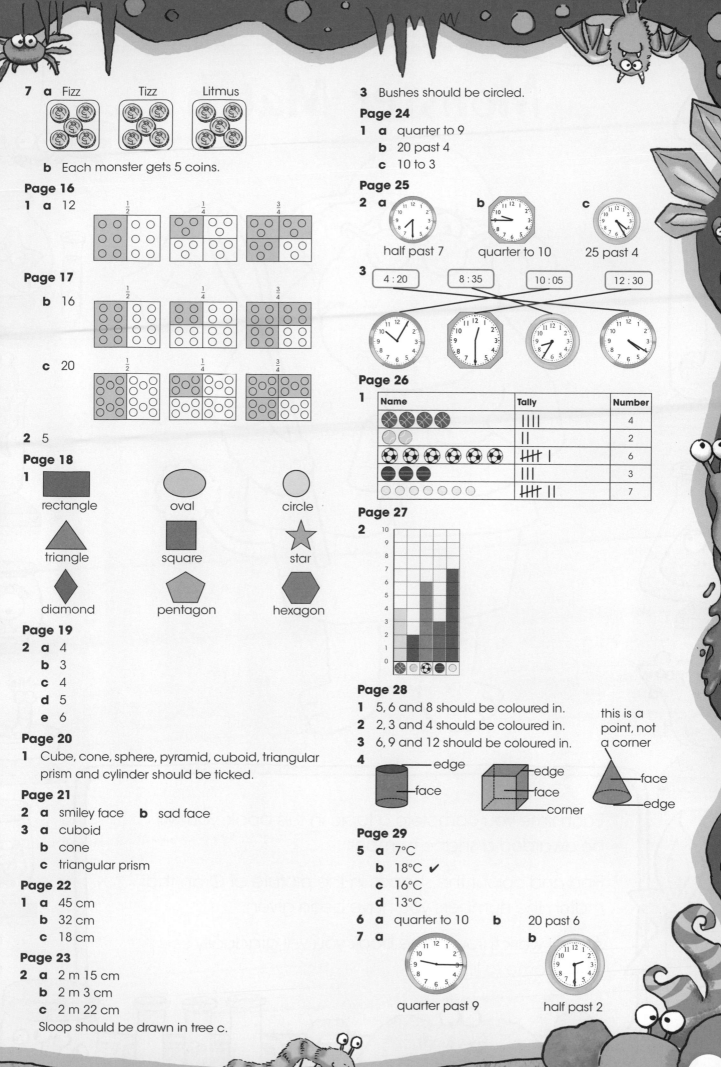

b Each monster gets 5 coins.

Page 16

1 a 12

$\frac{1}{2}$ $\frac{1}{4}$ $\frac{3}{4}$

Page 17

b 16

$\frac{1}{2}$ $\frac{1}{4}$ $\frac{3}{4}$

c 20

$\frac{1}{2}$ $\frac{1}{4}$ $\frac{3}{4}$

2 5

Page 18

1

rectangle   oval   circle

triangle   square   star

diamond   pentagon   hexagon

Page 19

2 a 4
  b 3
  c 4
  d 5
  e 6

Page 20

1 Cube, cone, sphere, pyramid, cuboid, triangular prism and cylinder should be ticked.

Page 21

2 a smiley face   **b** sad face
3 a cuboid
  b cone
  c triangular prism

Page 22

1 a 45 cm
  b 32 cm
  c 18 cm

Page 23

2 a 2 m 15 cm
  b 2 m 3 cm
  c 2 m 22 cm
Sloop should be drawn in tree c.

3 Bushes should be circled.

Page 24

1 a quarter to 9
  b 20 past 4
  c 10 to 3

Page 25

2 a half past 7   **b** quarter to 10   **c** 25 past 4

3 4 : 20   8 : 35   10 : 05   12 : 30

Page 26

1

Name	Tally	Number
	IIII	4
	II	2
	HHT I	6
	III	3
	HHT II	7

Page 27

2

Page 28

1 5, 6 and 8 should be coloured in.
2 2, 3 and 4 should be coloured in.
3 6, 9 and 12 should be coloured in.
4

this is a point, not a corner

edge — face   edge — face — corner   face — edge

Page 29

5 a 7°C
  b 18°C ✔
  c 16°C
  d 13°C
6 a quarter to 10   **b** 20 past 6
7 a quarter past 9   **b** half past 2

Monster Match

Each time you complete a topic in this book, you will be awarded a shape number.

Find and colour the shapes in the picture of Gran that match the numbers you have been given.

As you work through the book you will gradually see Gran come to life!